This book belongs to

....

make
believe
ideas

Hansel and Gretel

Key sound or spellings:
a, au, aw, oor, or, ore, ough, our

Secondary sounds: ch, el, mp

Written by Rosie Greening
Illustrated by Clare Fennell

Reading with phonics

How to use this book

The **Reading with phonics** series helps you to have fun with your child and to support their learning of phonics and reading. It is aimed at children who have learned the letter sounds and are building confidence in their reading.

Each title in the series focuses on a different key sound or blend of sounds. The entertaining retelling of the story repeats this sound frequently, and the different spellings for the sound or blend of sounds are highlighted in red type. The first activity at the back of the book provides practice in reading and using words containing this sound or blend of sounds. The key sound for **Hansel and Gretel** is or.

Start by reading the story to your child, asking them to join in with the refrain in bold. Next, encourage them to read the story with you. Give them a hand to decode tricky words.

Now look at the activity pages at the back of the book. These are intended for you and your child to enjoy together. Most are not activities to complete in pencil or pen, but by reading and talking or pointing.

The **Key sound** pages focus on one sound, and on the various different groups of letters that produce that sound. Encourage your child to read the different letter groups and complete the activity, so they become more aware of the variety of spellings there are for the same sound.

The **Letters together** pages look at three pairs or groups of letters and at the sounds they make as they work together. Help your child to read the words and trace the route on the word maps.

Rhyme is used a lot in these retellings. Whatever stage your child has reached in their learning of phonics, it is always good practice for them to listen carefully for sounds and find words that rhyme. The pages on **Rhyming words** take six words from the story and ask children to read and find other words that rhyme with them.

The **Key words** pages focus on a number of key words that occur regularly but can nonetheless be challenging. Many of these words are not sounded out following the rules of phonics and the easiest thing is for children to learn them by sight, so that they do not worry about decoding them. These pages encourage children to retell the story, practising key words as they do so.

The **Picture dictionary** page asks children to focus closely on nine words from the story. Encourage children to look carefully at each word, cover it with their hand, write it on a separate piece of paper, and finally, check it!

Do not complete all the activities at once – doing one each time you read will ensure that your child continues to enjoy the stories and the time you are spending together. **Have fun!**

Hansel and Gretel's family
were poor and hungry as can be.
They lived off cheese or mouldy bread,
but wished they had pork pies instead.

Hansel and Gretel are bored of bread.
They want to eat pork pies instead!

Their stepmum, Dawn, said, "That's enough!"
Then threw her fork down in a huff.
"Without the kids, we'd have more cash.
Let's drop them in the woods, then dash!"

Hansel and Gretel were nearby
and overheard Dawn's awful cry.
"We're toast!" cried Gretel, feeling scared.
But Hansel thought, "We'll be prepared."

Hansel and Gretel are bored of bread.
They want some cornbread now instead!

Next morning, armed with bread and cheese,
they followed Dawn out through the trees.
But Hansel dropped crumbs on the floor
to mark the path back to their door.

Hansel and Gretel are bored of bread.
They want some gorgeous cake instead!

9

Deep in the woods, Dawn sauntered back,
and so they searched for Hansel's track.
But all the crumbs of bread had gone –
the birds had gorged on every one!

10

Oh, no!

Hansel and Gretel are bored of bread.
They want some chocolate torte instead!

11

The pair were lost, and hungry too.
Poor Hansel cried, "What will we do?"
But then they saw something ahead . . .
a house made out of gingerbread!

Hansel and Gretel are bored of bread.

They want some toffee sauce instead!

13

The hungry children tore off treats,
gorged on the walls and nibbled sweets.
But then the door flung open wide,
and Witchy Nora stormed outside!

14

The witch looked down and gave a grin.
"Hello, my sweeties, do come in!
I've got more treats inside for you:
big strawberry cakes and popcorn too!"

Hansel and Gretel are bored of bread.
They want some popcorn snacks instead!

But once the children were indoors,
instead of treats, they just got chores.
For Nora had a secret plot
to eat them once her stove was hot!

Gretel was scared, but then she saw
a chest of treasure by the door.
She said to Nora, "You're so fat!
I bet you couldn't fit in that."

Hansel and Gretel are bored of bread.
They want some awesome treats instead!

The witch said, "Ha! I'll fit for sure,"
and poured the jewels out on the floor.

She crawled inside, and with a grin
the children quickly locked her in!

Hansel and Gretel are bored of bread.
They want tortilla chips instead!

Then, feeling extra brave and bold,
the pair stole Nora's jewels and gold.
They tore outside and ran all day
until, at last, they found their way.

Hansel and Gretel are bored of bread.
They want some strawberry treats instead!

The two burst through their parents' door,
and poured the haul out on the floor.
Their stepmum, Dawn, apologised,
and then they went to buy pork pies!

Hansel and Gretel are bored of bread.
At last, they have pork pies instead!

Key sound

There are several different groups of letters that make the **or** sound. Practise them by helping Hansel make some sentences. Use each word in the pies in a different sentence.

pour

thought   bought
fought

poor   floor
door

morning   Nora   for
storm   popcorn
torn

more chore
shore

saw   paw

strawberry
awful

Letters together

Look at these pairs of letters and say the sounds they make.

mp   el   ch

Follow the words that contain **mp** to help the children find some crumpets.

mp

stepmum

woods

lamp

crumbs

stomp

crumpets

bump

Follow the words that contain **el** to help Gretel find a pretzel.

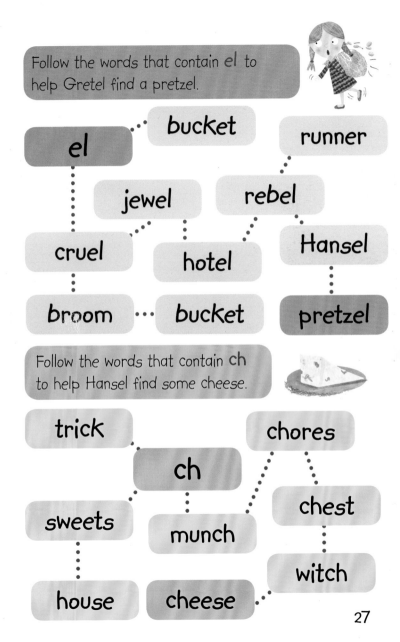

bucket

el

runner

jewel

rebel

cruel

hotel

Hansel

broom ···· bucket

pretzel

Follow the words that contain **ch** to help Hansel find some cheese.

trick

chores

ch

chest

sweets

munch

witch

house

cheese

Rhyming words

Read and say the words in the flowers, and then point to other words that rhyme with them.

pork	more
door	straw

poor

sweet	house
cake	eat

treat

watch	ditch
rich	trick

witch

28

Key words

Many common words can be tricky to sound out. Practise them by reading these sentences about the story. Now make more sentences using other key words from around the border.

Hansel **and** Gretel were very poor.

Their stepmum wasn't **very** nice.

Dawn led them **into** the woods.

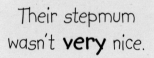

The children **saw** a gingerbread house.

called • their • looked • got • it

• children • off • a • if • very • made • are • put • we •

They **were** caught by a witch.

The witch made **them** do chores.

Gretel came up **with** a plan.

They tricked the witch and ran away.

They took **all** the witch's jewels!

all · saw · and · oh · them · let · wanted · mum · too · time · up · you · they ·

old · there · were · into · as · with · make · some

Picture dictionary

Look carefully at the pictures and the words.
Now cover the words, one at a time.
Can you remember how to write them?

birds   bread   chest

crumbs   door   house

pie   treasure   witch